budgetbooks

POP/ROC

Exclusive Distributors:
Music Sales Limited
8/9 Frith Street, London W1D 3JB, England.
Music Sales Pty Limited
120 Rothschild Avenue, Rosebery, NSW 2018, Australia.

Order No. HLE90001978
ISBN 1-84449-113-7
This book © Copyright 2003 by Hal Leonard Europe

Printed in the USA

Your Guarantee of Quality
As publishers, we strive to produce every book to the highest commercial standards.
The book has been carefully designed to minimise awkward page turns and to make playing from it a real pleasure.
Throughout, the printing and binding have been planned to ensure a sturdy, attractive publication which should give years of enjoyment.
If your copy fails to meet our high standards, please inform us and we will gladly replace it.

www.musicsales.com

This publication is not authorised for sale in the
United States of America and/or Canada

Hal Leonard Europe
Distributed by Music Sales

CONTENTS

ADIA

Words and Music by SARAH McLACHLAN
and PIERRE MARCHAND

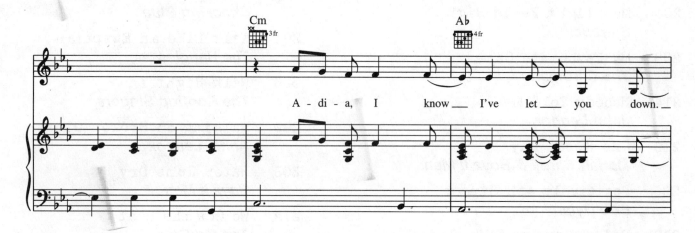

BAKER STREET

Words and Music by
GERRY RAFFERTY

Verse 1. Wind-ing your way down on Bak - er Street.___
2. This cit-y des - sert makes you feel so cold.___ He's got

Verse 3: Way down the street there's a lot in his place,
He opens his door he's got that look on his face
And he asks you where you've been
You tell him who you've seen and you talk about anything.

Verse 4: He's got this dream about buyin' some land he's gonna
Give up the booze and the one night stands and
Then you'll settle down with some quiet little town
And forget about everything.

Chorus 3: But you know you'll always keep movin'
You know he's never gonna stop movin'
'Cause he's rollin' he's the rollin' stone.

Chorus 4: When you wake up it's a new mornin'
The sun is shinin', it's a new mornin'
And you're goin', you're goin' home.

AFRICA

Words and Music by DAVID PAICH
and JEFF PORCARO

ANGEL

Words and Music by
SARAH McLACHLAN

Original key: D♭ major. This edition has been transposed down one half-step to be more playable.

BABY WHAT A BIG SURPRISE

Words and Music by
PETER CETERA

Right be-fore my ver-y _____ eyes _____ I thought _____
Yes-ter-day it seemed to _____ me _____ my life _____

_____ that _ you were on-ly fak-in' it, and like _____
_____ was _ noth-ing more than wast-ed time, but here _____

_____ be-fore my heart was tak-in' it. _____
_____ to-day you soft-ly changed _ my mind. _

BAD, BAD LEROY BROWN

Words and Music by
JIM CROCE

Moderate Boogie-Rock tempo

Le - roy more than trou - ble, you see he stand _ 'bout six - foot - four. _
cus - tom Con - ti - nen - tal, he got a El - do - ra - do, too. _
cast his eyes up - on _ her, and the trou - ble soon be - gan, _

All the down - town la - dies call him
He got a thir - ty - two gun _ in his
and Le - roy Brown, _ he learned a

"tree - top lov - er," all the men just call him "Sir." _
pock - et for fun, _ he got a ra - zor in his shoe. _
les - son 'bout mess - in' with the wife of a jeal - ous man. _

And he's bad, _ bad Le - roy Brown, _ the

BANG A GONG
(Get It On)

Words and Music by
MARC BOLAN

D.S. and Fade
(verse 4)

2. You're built like a car
   You've got a hub cap diamond star halo
   You're built like a car oh yeah
   You're an untamed youth that's the truth
   With your cloak full of eagles
   You're dirty sweet and you're my girl.

3. You're windy and wild
   You've got the blues in your shoes and your stockings
   You're windy and wild oh yeah
   You're built like a car
   You've got a hub cap diamond star halo
   You're dirty sweet and you're my girl.

4. You're dirty and sweet
   Clad in black, don't look back and I love you.
   You're dirty and sweet oh yeah
   You dance when you walk
   So let's dance, take a chance, understand me
   You're dirty sweet and you're my girl.

To Chorus and Fade

CRIMSON AND CLOVER

Words and Music by TOMMY JAMES
and PETER LUCIA

BARBARA ANN

Words and Music by
FRED FASSERT

BARELY BREATHING

Words and Music by
DUNCAN SHEIK

Moderately

ing. I see it all _ too clear. _ I on - ly taste _ the sa - line when I kiss a - way _ your tears. _

DIGNITY

Words and Music by
RICKY ROSS

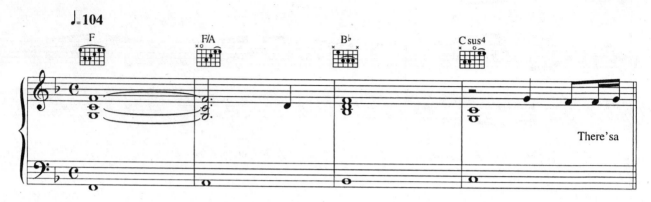

There's a

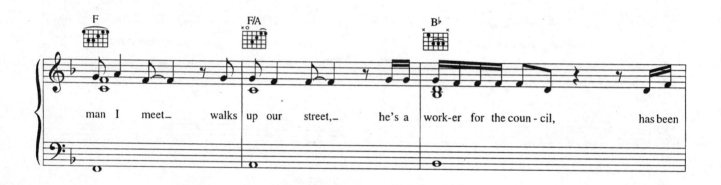

man I meet— walks up our street,— he's a work-er for the coun-cil, has been

twen-ty years— and he takes no lip from no-bo-dy and lit-ter off the gut-ter.

Puts it in a bag and ne-ver thinks to mut-ter. And he packs his lunch in a Sun-blest bag, the

Lyrics ad lib. to fade:
And I'm thinking about home …

And I'm thinking about faith …

And I'm thinking about work …

And I'm thinking about how good it would be
To be here some day,

On a ship called Dignity,
A ship called Diginity,

That ship.

DIZZY

Words and Music by TOMMY ROE
and FREDDY WELLER

DO WAH DIDDY DIDDY

Words and Music by JEFF BARRY
and ELLIE GREENWICH

Moderately

There he was, __ just a walk-in' down the street, Sing-in' do wah did - dy did - dy,
fore I knew __ it he was walk-in' next to me, Sing-in' do wah did - dy did - dy,

down did - dy do; Pop-pin' his fin - gers and a shuf-fl-in' his feet, Sing-in'
down did - dy do; He took __ my hand _____ just as nat - 'ral as can be, Sing-in'

do wah did - dy did - dy, down did - dy do. He looked good, (Yeah, yeah) He looked
do wah did - dy did - dy, down did - dy do. We walked on, (Yeah, yeah) To my

DON'T PANIC

Words and Music by GUY BERRYMAN,
JON BUCKLAND, WILL CHAMPION and CHRIS MARTIN

1, 2. Bones,   sink - ing like stones,   all___ that we've   fought___ for.___
(Verse 3 Instrumental)

Homes,   pla - ces we've grown,   all___ of us are

Oh, all— that I know, there's no-thing here to run from,– cos

yeah, ev - 'ry - bo - dy here's got some - bo - dy to lean on.—

DON'T SPEAK

Words and Music by ERIC STEFANI
and GWEN STEFANI

DOWN IN THE BOONDOCKS

Words and Music by
JOE SOUTH

FLOWERS IN THE WINDOW

Words and Music by
FRAN HEALY

1. When I ___ first held ___ you I ___ was cold, ___
(Verses 2 & 3 see block lyrics)

Verse 2:
There is no reason to feel bad
But there are many seasons to feel glad, sad, mad
It's just a bunch of feelings that we have to hold
But I am here to help you with the load.

Wow, look at you now *etc.*

Verse 3:
So now we're here and now is fine
So far away from there and there is time, time, time
To plant new seeds and watch them grow
So there'll be flowers in the window when we go.

Wow, look at us now *etc.*

GOOD VIBRATIONS

Words and Music by BRIAN WILSON
and MIKE LOVE

A GIRL LIKE YOU

Words and Muisc by
EDWYN COLLINS

1. I've
(Verse 2 see block lyric)

nev- er known a girl like you be- fore,—

yes you've come a-long, and I've nev-er met a girl like

you be-fore.———

Repeat ad lib. to fade

Verse 2:
You give me just a taste so I want more,
Now my hands are bleeding and my knees are raw,
Now you've got me crawlin' crawlin' on the floor,
And I've never known a girl like you before.

GOD ONLY KNOWS

Words and Music by BRIAN WILSON
and TONY ASHER

GOODBYE TO LOVE

Words and Music by RICHARD CARPENTER
and JOHN BETTIS

song, and it's good-bye to love. ___ I'll say good-

bye to love. ___ Ah. _____

Repeat ad lib. and Fade

Ah. _____

THE GREAT PRETENDER

Words and Music by
BUCK RAM

GREEN ONIONS

Written by AL JACKSON, JR., LEWIS STEINBERG,
BOOKER T. JONES and STEVE CROPPER

HOW WILL I KNOW

Words and Music by GEORGE MERRILL,
SHANNON RUBICAM and NARADA MICHAEL WALDEN

Original key: Gb major. This edition has been transposed up one half-step to be more playable.

* Cues 2nd time only

I AM WOMAN

Words by HELEN REDDY
Music by RAY BURTON

I DON'T WANT TO WAIT

Words and Music by
PAULA COLE

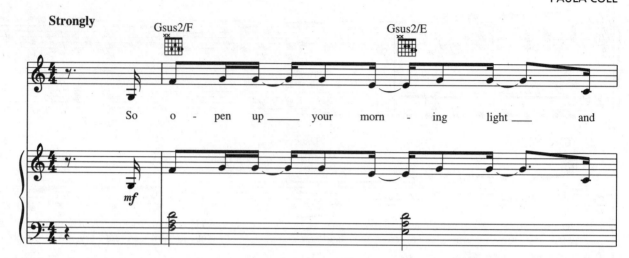

I HOPE YOU DANCE

Words and Music by TIA SILLERS
and MARK D. SANDERS

I WILL ALWAYS LOVE YOU

Words and Music by
DOLLY PARTON

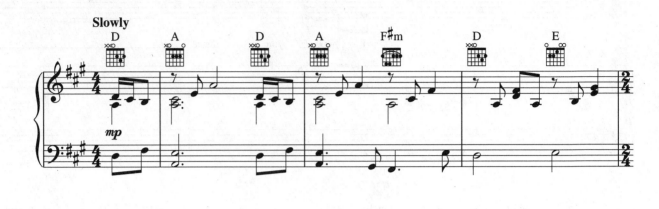

If I should stay, I would on-ly be in your
sweet mem-o-ries, that's all I am tak-ing with
hope life treats you kind and I hope that you have all that you

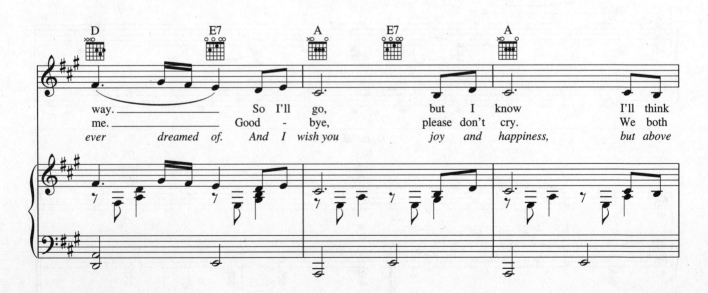

way. So I'll go, but I know I'll think
me. Good-bye, please don't cry. We both
ever dreamed of. And I wish you joy and happiness, but above

I'M EVERY WOMAN

Words and Music by NICKOLAS ASHFORD
and VALERIE SIMPSON

I'm ev - 'ry wom - an. It's all ___ in ___

'cause I'm the one. _____ You just ask me,

ooh, _____ and it shall be done. _____ And don't both - er

to ___ com - pare. _____ 'Cause I got it. _____

Cm   Gm7   **1.,2.** Fm7   Ab/Bb   **3.** Fm7   Ab/Bb

Whoa,   whoa,   whoa.   whoa,

I'M OUTTA LOVE

I'M OUTTA LOVE

Words and Music by ANASTACIA,
SAM WATTERS and LOUIS BIANCANIELLO

Verse 2:
Said how many times
Have I tried to turn this love around
But every time
You just let me down
Come on be a man about it
You'll survive
Sure that you can work it out alright
Tell me yesterday did you know
I'd be the one to let you go?
And you know.

I'm outta love *etc.*

JACK AND DIANE

Words and Music by
JOHN MELLENCAMP

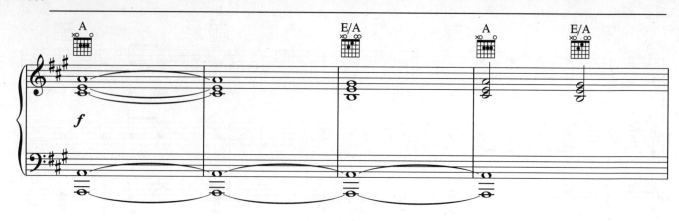

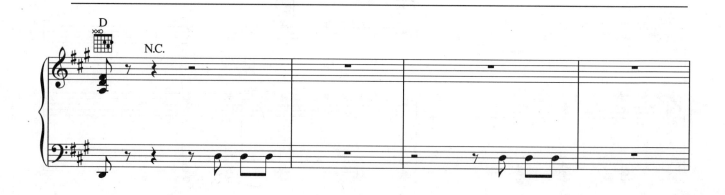

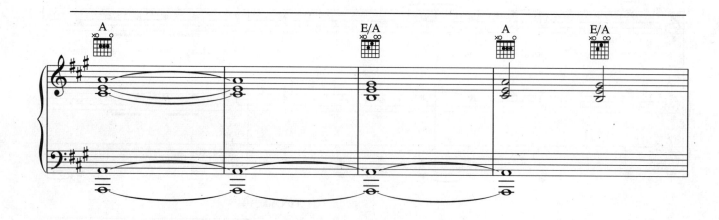

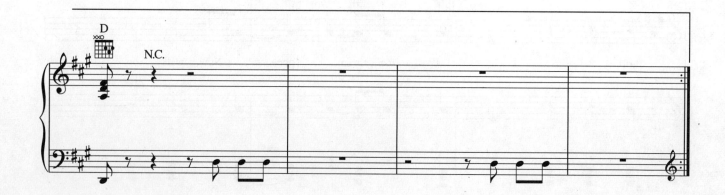

change is com - in' 'round real soon, make us wom - en and men.

C   E/A   D/A   E/A

A   E/A   D/A   A

D.S. al Coda

CODA

A   E

A lit - tle

Repeat and Fade

IF I EVER LOSE MY FAITH IN YOU

Music and Lyrics by
STING

You could say I   lost__ my faith in__ sci-
Some would say I was__ a   lost__ man in a__ lost
I nev-er saw no   mir-a-cle of sci-ence

ence   and prog - ress.
world.

JOY TO THE WORLD

Words and Music by
HOYT AXTON

LA BAMBA

By RITCHIE VALENS

LET'S HEAR IT FOR THE BOY

from the Paramount Motion Picture FOOTLOOSE

Words by DEAN PITCHFORD
Music by TOM SNOW

LIFTED

Words and Music by PAUL TUCKER,
EMMANUEL BAIYEWU and MARTIN BRAMMER

Verse 2:

It's undisturbable, the peace we've found
In a bright blue space up above the clouds.
Where everything is understandable,
You don't have to say anything too loud.

When our luck runs out again,
Brought back down to solid ground
I wouldn't say I'm mad about the rain
But we'll get through it anyway.
We'll get back to the stars again.

THE LIFE OF RILEY

Words and Music by
IAN BROUDIE

Lost in the Milk-y Way,___ smile at the emp-ty sky___

To Coda ⊕

in this world we've___ got to find the time___

for the life of Ri - ley.

All this world___ is a cra - zy ride,___ just take___

D.%. al Coda

___ your seat___ and hold___ on tight.___ So

⊕ Coda

Verse 2:
From cradles and sleepless nights
You breathe in life forever
And stare at the world
From deep under eiderdown.

LIGHT MY FIRE

Words and Music by
THE DOORS

A LITTLE TIME

Words and Music by PAUL HEATON
and DAVID ROTHERAY

(M) 1. I need a lit-tle ___ ___ time ___ to think it ov-er. I need a lit-tle space ___ just on my

(Verses 2 & 3 see block lyrics)

To Coda

I've had a lit-tle___ time.___

I've had a lit-tle___

___ time.___

I've had a lit-tle___

rit.

time.___

F

Verse 2:

(M) I need a little room to find myself
     I need a little space to work it out
     I need a little room all alone
     I need a little…

(F) You need a little room for your big head
     Don't you, don't you?
     You need a little space for a thousand beds
     Won't you, won't you?
     Lips that promise, fear the worst
     Tongue so sharp the bubble burst
     Just into unjust.

Verse 3:

(M) I've had a little time to find the truth
     I've had a little room to check what's wrong
     I've had a little time and I still love you
     I've had a little…

(F) You had a little time and you had a little fun
     Didn't you, didn't you?
     When you had yours do you think I had none
     Do you, do you?
     The freedom that you wanted back
     Is yours for good, I hope you're glad
     Sad into unsad.

     I had a little time to think it over *etc*.

LOOKS LIKE WE MADE IT

Words and Music by RICHARD KERR
and WILL JENNINGS

There you are, _____ look-in' just the same as you did last time I
Love's so strange, _____ play-ing hide and seek with hearts and al-ways

touched you. And here I am, _____ close to get-tin' tan-gled up _____ in-side the
hurt-ing. And we're the fools, _____ stand-ing close e-nough to touch _____ those burn-ing

thought of you. Do you love him as much as I _____ love her? And will that love be
mem-o-ries. And if I hold you for the sake of all _____ those times love made us lose our

MAKE IT EASY ON YOURSELF

Lyric by HAL DAVID
Music by BURT BACHARACH

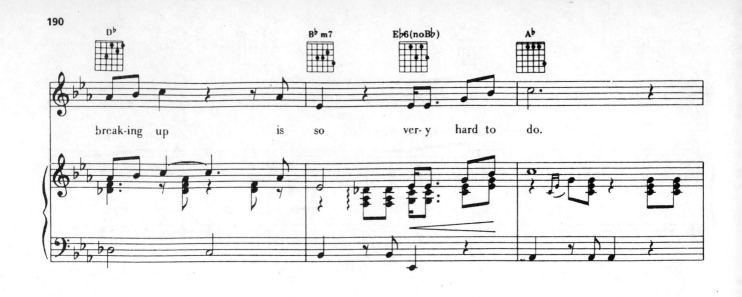

break-ing up   is   so   ver-y   hard to   do.

And   if   the   way   I   hold   you   can't   com-pare to { his / her }   ca-

ress _____   no   words of   con-so-la-tion

will make me miss you less. _____ My dar - ling,

if this is good - bye, _____ I just know I'm gon - na cry _____

so, run to {him / her} be - fore you start cry - in'

too; And make it eas - y on your - self, _____

ME AND YOU AND A DOG NAMED BOO

Words and Music by
LOBO

MELLOW YELLOW

MELLOW YELLOW

Words and Music by
DONOVAN LEITCH

Yel - low.—

Yel - low,—

they call me Mel - low

Repeat to fade

Verse 2:
I'm just mad about Fourteen,
Fourteen's mad about me.
I'm just mad about Fourteen,
She's just mad about me.

TO CHORUS:

Verse 3:
Born high, forever to fly,
Wind velocity: nil
Born high, forever to fly,
If you want your cup I will fill.

TO CHORUS:

Verse 4:
Instrumental

Verse 5:
Electrical banana
Is going to be a sudden craze.
Electrical banana
Is bound to be the very next phase.

TO CHORUS:

Verse 6:
I'm just mad about Saffron
I'm just mad about her.
I'm just mad about Saffron
She's just mad about me.

TO CHORUS:

MONDAY, MONDAY

Words and Music by
JOHN PHILLIPS

MONY, MONY

Words and Music by BOBBY BLOOM,
TOMMY JAMES, RITCHIE CORDELL
and BO GENTRY

Here she comes now, say, Mo-ny, Mo-ny. ____
Wake me, shake me, Mo-ny, Mo-ny. ____

Shoot 'em down, turn a-round,
Shot-gun git it done,

come on, Mo-ny. ____
come on, Mo-ny. ____

MOONLIGHT FEELS RIGHT

Words and Music by
MICHAEL BLACKMAN

Em7 ... **C6**

fi - n'lly made a trick - y French con - nec - tion; you winked and gave me your O. K.___
play the ra - di - o on south - ern sta - tions, 'cause south - ern belles are hell at night.

guess you know I'm giv - ing you a warn - ing, 'cause me and moon are itch - ing to play.___

Cmaj7 ... **A/B**

I'll take you on a trip be - side the o - cean and
You say you came to Bal - ti - more from Old Miss, a

I'll take you on a trip be - side the o - cean and

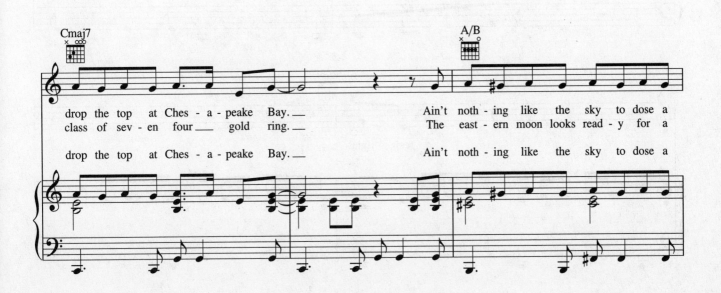

Cmaj7 ... **A/B**

drop the top at Ches - a - peake Bay.___ Ain't noth - ing like the sky to dose a
class of sev - en four___ gold ring.___ The east - ern moon looks read - y for a

drop the top at Ches - a - peake Bay.___ Ain't noth - ing like the sky to dose a

MY FAVOURITE GAME

Words by NINA PERSSON
Music by PETER SVENSSON

1. I don't know what you're look-ing for,———— you have-n't found it ba-by, that's for sure.—
(Verse 2 see block lyric)

Verse 2:
I only know what I've been working for
Another you so I could love you more
I really thought that I could take you there
But my experiment is not getting us anywhere

I had a vision I could turn you right
A stupid mission and a lethal fight
I should have seen it when my hope was new
My heart is black and my body is blue.

And I'm losing *etc.*

NOBODY TOLD ME

Words and Music by
JOHN LENNON

1. Now

ev'-ry-bo-dy's talk - in' and no one says a word,— now ev'-ry-bo-dy's mak-in' love_ and
(Verse 2 see block lyric)

no-one real-ly cares_ there's nas-ties in the bath-room just____ be-low the stairs.__

No-bo-dy told me there'd be days like these,

no-bo-dy told me there'd be days like these,

no-bo-dy told me there'd be days like these.

Strange days in - deed,___ strange days in - deed.___

D.%. al Coda
To Coda ⊕

⊕ **Coda**

Repeat to fade

Verse 2:
Everybody's running
And no one makes a move,
Now everybody's a winner
And nothing left to lose,
There's a little yellow island
To the north of Katmandu.

Everybody's flying
And no one leaves the ground,
Well everybody's crying
And no one makes a sound,
There's a place for it in movies
You just gotta lay around.

Nobody told me there'd be days like these… *x3*
Strange days indeed,
Most peculiar mama.

Verse 3:
Eveybody's smoking
And no one's getting high,
Everybody's flying
And never touch the sky,
There's UFO's over New York
And I ain't too surprised.

Nobody told me there'd be days like these… *x3*
Strange days indeed,
Most peculiar mama.

ONE SWEET DAY

Words and Music by MARIAH CAREY, WALTER AFANASIEFF,
SHAWN STOCKMAN, MICHAEL McCARY,
NATHAN MORRIS and WANYA MORRIS

SHEILA

Words and Music by
TOMMY ROE

like - a lit - tle Shei - la. Her name drives me in - sane.

Sweet lit - tle girl, that's my lit - tle Shei - la; man, this lit - tle girl is fine.

— Me and Shei - la __ go for a ride. Oh, __

oh, oh, oh, I feel - a fun - ny in - side. Then lit - tle Shei - la __

POSITIVELY 4th STREET

By BOB DYLAN

227

Verse 3:
I know the reason
That you talk behind my back
I used to be among the crowd
You're in with.

Do you take me for such a fool
To think I'd make contact
With the one who tries to hide
What he don't know to begin with?

Verse 4:
You see me on the street
You always act surprised
You say, "How are you?" "Good luck"
But you don't mean it.

When you know as well as me
You'd rather see me paralyzed
Why don't you just come out once
And scream it.

Verse 5:
No, I do not feel that good
When I see the heartbreaks you embrace
If I was a master thief
Perhaps I'd rob them.

And now I know you're dissatisfied
With your position and your place
Don't you understand
It's not my problem.

Verse 6:
I wish that for just one time
You could stand inside my shoes
And just for that one moment
I could be you.

Yes, I wish that for just one time
You could stand inside my shoes
You'd know what a drag it is
To see you.

RAINY DAYS AND MONDAYS

Lyrics by PAUL WILLIAMS
Music by ROGER NICHOLS

RESPECT YOURSELF

Words and Music by MACK RICE
and LUTHER INGRAM

don't give a heck a - bout the man with the Bi - ble in his hand,
talk - in' 'bout the pres - i - dent won't stop air pol - lu - tion.

just get out the way and let the gen - tle - man do his thing.____
Put your hand o'er your mouth when you cough that - 'll help the so - lu -

tion.
Oh,__ you cuss a - round wom - en folk,
You the kind of gen - tle - man

want ev - 'ry - thing your way.____
don't e - ven know their name.____
Take the
Then you're

sheet off your face, boy. It's a brand new day. ___
dumb e - nough to think it - 'll make ___ you a big ol' man.

Re - spect your - self. ___

Re - spect your - self. ___

Re - spect your - self. ___

Re - spect your - self. ___

G7

If you don't re - spect your - self, ain't no - bod - y gon - na give a good, good

SATURDAY NIGHT'S ALRIGHT
(For Fighting)

Words and Music by ELTON JOHN
and BERNIE TAUPIN

THE SIGN

Words and Music by buddha,
joker, jenny and linn

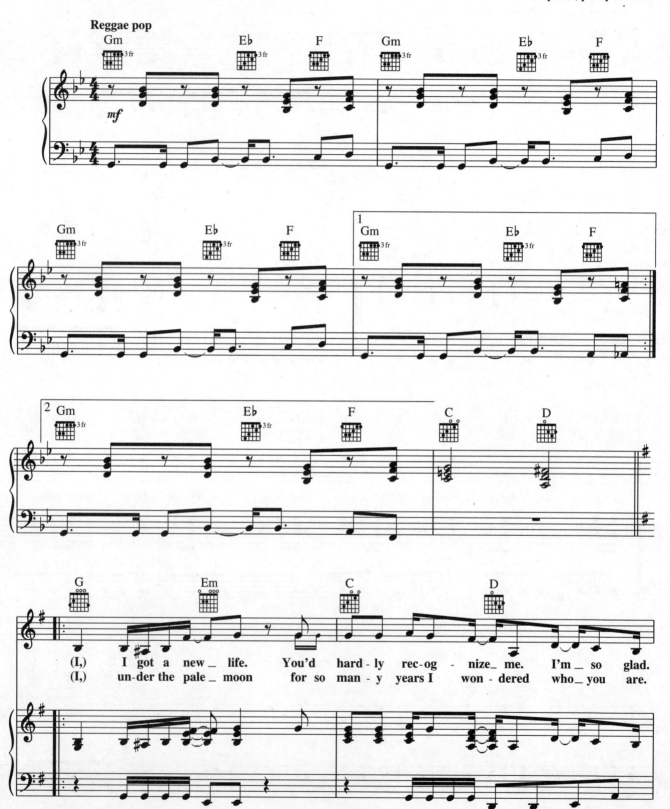

STAND BY ME

Words and Music by BEN E. KING,
JERRY LEIBER and MIKE STOLLER

SURVIVOR

Words and Music by BEYONCE KNOWLES,
ANTHONY DENT and MATTHEW KNOWLES

Original key: Ab minor. This edition has been transposed up one half-step to be more playable.

SUNSHINE SUPERMAN

SUNSHINE SUPERMAN

Words and Music by
DONOVAN LEITCH

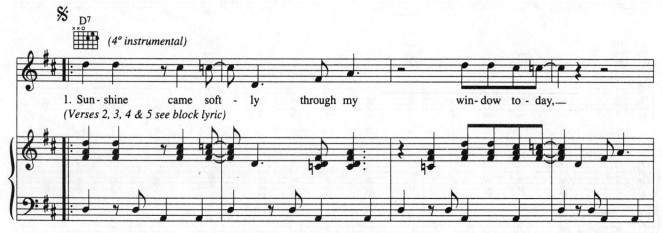

1. Sun-shine came soft-ly through my win-dow to-day,—
(Verses 2, 3, 4 & 5 see block lyric)

could have tripped out ea-sy but I've changed my ways,—

⊕ **Coda**

ad lib. to fade

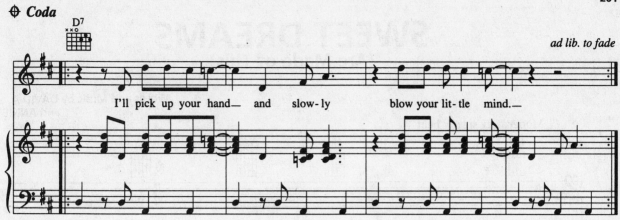

I'll pick up your hand— and slow-ly   blow your lit-tle   mind.—

Verse 2:
Superman and Green Lantern ain't got nothing on me
I can make like a turtle and dive for pearls in the sea
You can just sit there thinking on your velvet throne
I've followed the rainbow so you can have all your own.

'Cause I've made my mind up you're going to be mine.
I'll tell you right now
Any trick in the book now baby that I can find.

Verse 3:
Everybody's hustling just to have a little scene
When I said we'd be cool I think that you know what I mean.
We stood on a beach at sunset, do you remember when?
I know a beach where baby, it never ends.

When you've made your mind up forever to be mine.
(to 3rd ending)

Verse 4:
Instrumental

Verse 5:
Superman and Green Lantern ain't got nothing on me
I can make like a turtle and dive for pearls in the sea
You can just sit there thinking on your velvet throne
I've followed the rainbow so you can have all your own.

When you've made your mind up forever to be mine.
(to 5th ending)

SWEET DREAMS
(Are Made of This)

Words and Music by DAVID A. STEWART
and ANNIE LENNOX

TAKE ON ME

Music by PAL WAAKTAAR and MAGNE FURUHOLMNE
Words by PAL WAAKTAAR,
MAGNE FURUHOLMNE and MORTON HARKET

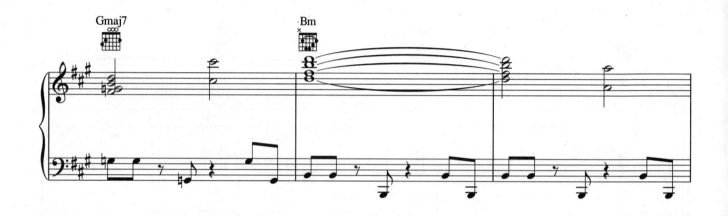

D.S. al Coda
(Take Repeat)

TEARIN' UP MY HEART

Words and Music by MAX MARTIN
and KRISTIAN LUNDIN

TEQUILA

By CHUCK RIO

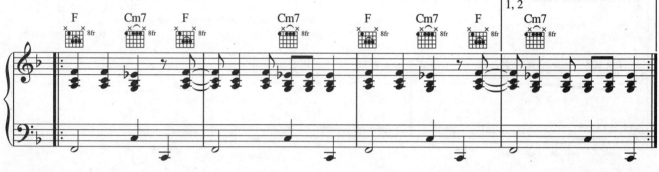

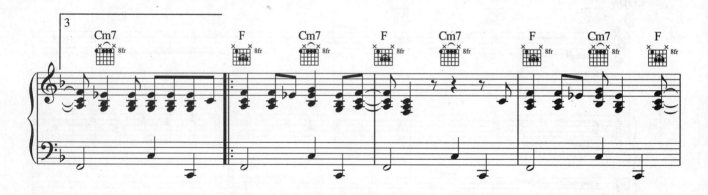

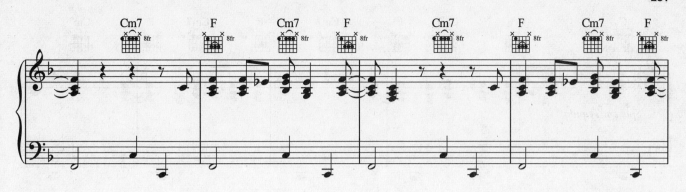

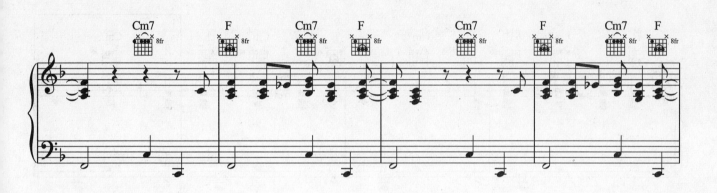

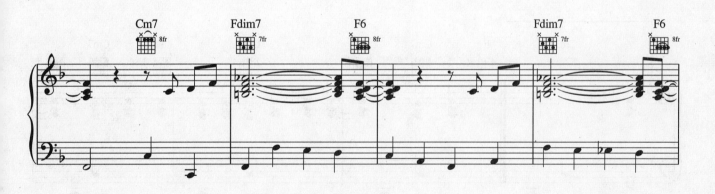

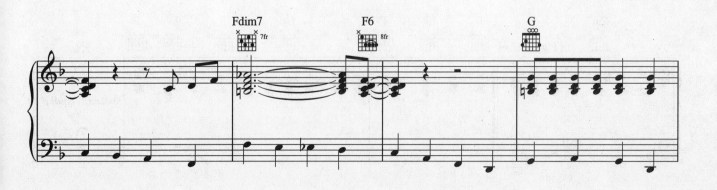

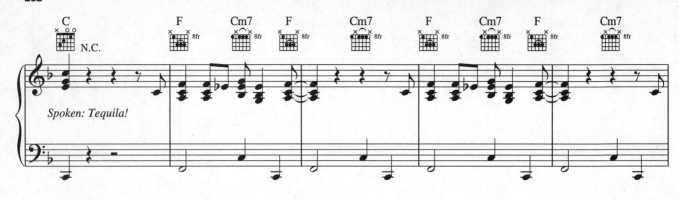

Spoken: Tequila!

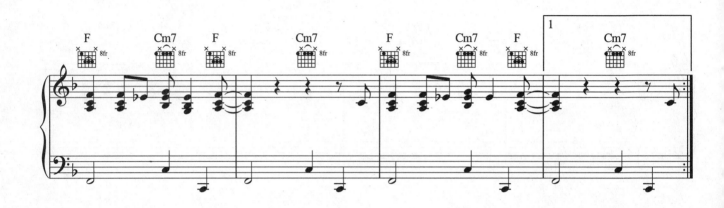

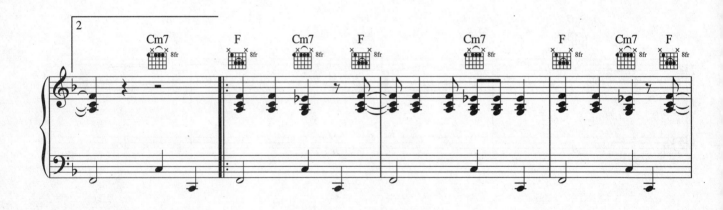

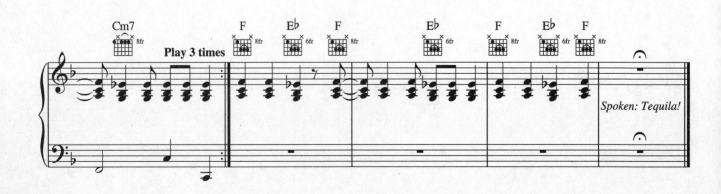

Spoken: Tequila!

TRACES

Words and Music by J.R. COBB
and BUDDY BUIE

TOP OF THE WORLD

Words and Music by JOHN BETTIS
and RICHARD CARPENTER

Such a feel-in's com-in' o-ver me, _____ there is
Some-thing in ___ the wind has learned my name, _____ and it's

VENUS

Words and Music by
ROBERT VAN LEEUWEN

god - dess on a moun - tain top —— was

(Verse 2 see block lyric)

⊕ Coda

your de - sire

Ah!   ah!

ah!   ah!   ah!   ah!   ah!   ah!

Repeat to fade

Verse 2:
Her weapons were her crystal eyes
Making every man feel mad
Black as a dark night she was
Got what no one else had.

WALK LIKE AN EGYPTIAN

Words and Music by
LIAM STERNBERG

1. All the old paint - ings on ___ the
2. All the ba - zaar men by ___ the
3.–7. *(See additional lyrics)*

tomb, they do ___ the sand dance, don't _ you know. If they move too
Nile, they got ___ the mon - ey on ___ a bet. Gold croc - o -

quick, (oh ___ way oh,) they're fall - ing down like a dom - i - no.
diles, (oh ___ way oh,) they snap _ their teeth

1, 3, 5, 6

Additional Lyrics

3. The blond waitresses take their trays.
   They spin around and they cross the floor.
   They've got the moves, oh way oh.
   You drop your drink, then they bring you more.

4. All the schoolkids so sick of books,
   They like the punk and the metal band.
   Then the buzzer rings, oh way oh,
   They're walking like an Egyptian.

5. Slide your feet up the street, bend your back.
   Shift your arm, then you pull it back.
   Life's hard, you know, oh way oh,
   So strike a pose on a Cadillac.

6. If you want to find all the cops,
   They're hanging out in the donut shop.
   They sing and dance, oh way oh.
   They spin the club, cruise down the block.

7. All the Japanese with their yen,
   The party boys call the Kremlin.
   And the Chinese know, oh way oh,
   They walk the line like Egyptians.

WALKING ON BROKEN GLASS

Words and Music by
ANNIE LENNOX

WALK RIGHT IN

Words and Music by GUS CANNON
and H. WOODS

Slowly, with strong beat

1. Walk Right In, ____ set right ____ down, ____ Dad-dy, let your mind roll on.

2. Walk Right In, ____ set right ____ down, ____ Ba-by, let your hair hang down.

Walk Right In, ____ set right ____ down, ____

Walk Right In, ____ set right ____ down, ____

WATER RUNS DRY

Words and Music by
BABYFACE

Moderately

We don't e-ven talk an-y-more. _____
Now they can see the tears in our eyes, _____

And we don't e-ven know what we ar - gue a - bout. _____
but we de-ny the pain that lies deep in our hearts. _____

no chord

Don't ev-en say, "I love you," no more, _____
Well, may-be that's a pain we can't hide, _____

WE GOT THE BEAT

Words and Music by
CHARLOTTE CAFFEY

See the peo - ple walk - ing down the street;
See the kids just get - ting out of school.
Go - go mu - sic real - ly makes us dance.

fall in line just watch - ing all their feet.___ They don't know where___
They can't wait to hang___ out and be cool.___ Hang a - round 'til quar -
Do the po - ny; puts___ us in a trance.___ Do the watusi, just___

___ they want to go, but they walk - ing in time. They}
ter af - ter twelve. That's when they fall in line They} got the beat,___
___ give us a chance. That's when we fall in line. 'Cause we}

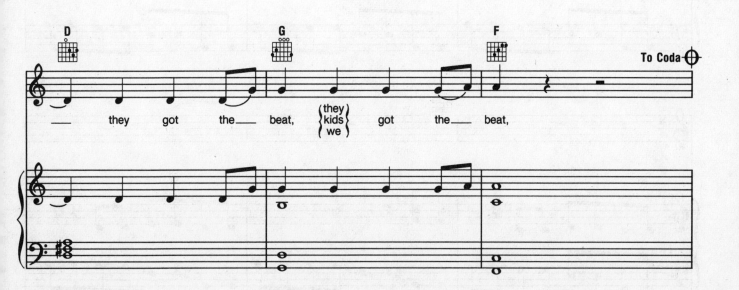

they got the___ beat, {they}{kids}{we} got the___ beat,

To Coda

WHEN YOU'RE GONE

Words and Music by BRYAN ADAMS
and ELIOT KENNEDY

A WHITER SHADE OF PALE

Words and Music by KEITH REID
and GARY BROOKER

Lyrics:

We skipped the light__ fan-dan-go,_____ turned cart-wheels 'cross the
She said, "I'm home__ on shore leave,"_____ though in truth we__ were at
She said,"There is__ no rea-son,_____ and the truth is__ plain to

floor;__
sea;__ I was feel-ing kind of sea-sick,
see,"__ So I took her by the look-ing glass
But I wan-dered through my play-ing cards

WINCHESTER CATHEDRAL

Words and Music by
GEOFF STEPHENS

326

YESTERDAY ONCE MORE

Words and Music by JOHN BETTIS
and RICHARD CARPENTER

When I was young I'd lis-ten to the ra-di-o,___ wait-in'
back on how it was in years gone by___ and the

for my fa-v'rite songs.___ When they played, I'd sing a- long;___
good times that I had,___ makes to-day seem rath-er sad;___

it made me smile.___
so much has changed.___

Those were such
It was

YOU SANG TO ME

Words and Music by CORY ROONEY
and MARC ANTHONY

334